For every small child who likes to sing, and mothers who wish to accompany them, here are twenty-six favorite nursery songs. "Pop Goes the Weasel," "Frere Jacques," "The Farmer in the Dell," "Jingle Bells" —they are all here and many more.

Charmingly illustrated and complete with simple piano arrangements, this is the ideal first book of music for any child.

FAVORITE NURSERY SONGS

Compiled by PHYLLIS BROWN OHANIAN

Illustrated by MARJORIE TORREY

Published in New York by Random House, Inc., and simultaneously in Toronto, Canada, by Random House of Canada, Limited.
Manufactured in the United States of America.
Library of Congress Catalog Card Number: M56-1004.
Music autographing by Maxwell Weaner.

RANDOM HOUSE, NEW YORK

Row, Row, Row (Round)

Traditional

Vigorously

Row, row, row your boat Gent - ly down the stream. —

Mer - ri - ly, mer - ri - ly, mer - ri - ly, mer - ri - ly, Life is but a dream. —

This round is fun for the whole family to sing. Divide the singers into two groups, being sure that at least one good voice is in each group. The first group starts, and when it reaches the fourth bar (at the word "Merrily") the second group starts in at the beginning of the song. Both groups continue singing the song through without a break 3 or 4 times

Oh, Where Has My Little Dog Gone?

Nursery Rhyme

Old Tune

Oh, where, oh where has my lit-tle dog gone? Oh,
where, oh where can he be?_____ With his ears cut short and his
tail cut long, Oh, where, oh where can he be?_____

The Autoharp may be used with this song.

Lazy Mary

Mother Goose

Singing Game

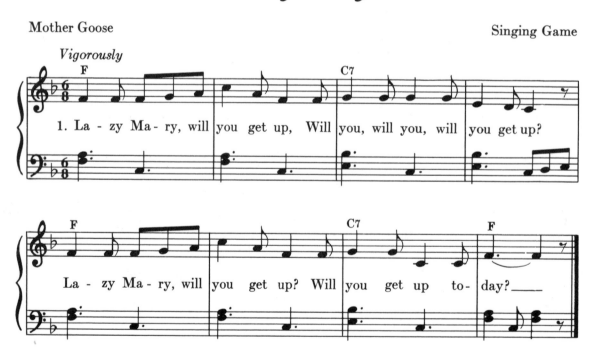

The Autoharp may be used with this song.

2. No, Mother, I won't get up;
   I won't, I won't, I won't get up!
   No, Mother, I won't get up;
   I won't get up today!

Sing a Song of Sixpence

Mother Goose

J. W. Elliott

Not too slow

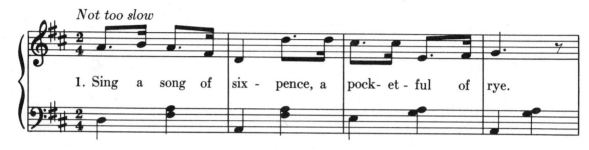

1. Sing a song of six - pence, a pock- et - ful of rye.

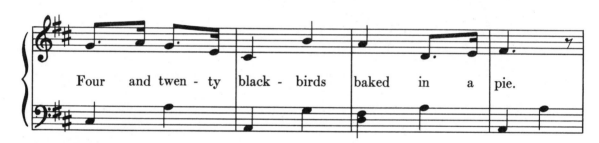

Four and twen - ty black - birds baked in a pie.

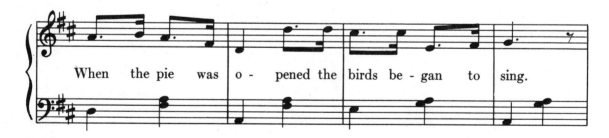

When the pie was o - pened the birds be - gan to sing.

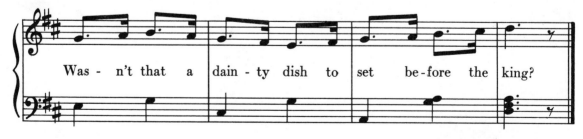

Was - n't that a dain - ty dish to set be - fore the king?

2. The king was in his counting house,
   Counting out his money;
   The queen was in the parlor,
   Eating bread and honey.

The maid was in the garden,
Hanging out the clothes;
Along came a blackbird
And nipped off her nose!

8

Pussy Cat, Pussy Cat

Mother Goose

J. W. Elliott

Earnestly

Pus - sy Cat, Pus - sy Cat, where have you been?

I've been to Lon - don to vis - it the Queen.

Pus - sy Cat, Pus - sy Cat, what did you there? I

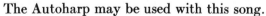

fright - ened a lit - tle mouse un - der her chair.

The Autoharp may be used with this song.

The Muffin Man

Old English Nursery Jingle

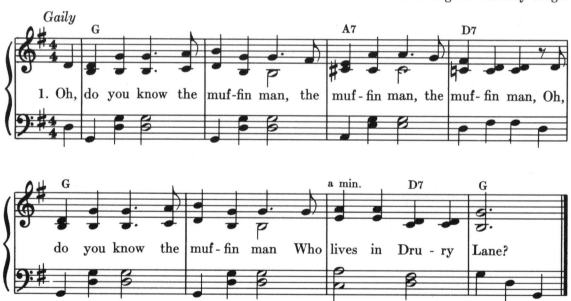

1. Oh, do you know the muf-fin man, the muf-fin man, the muf-fin man, Oh, do you know the muf-fin man Who lives in Dru-ry Lane?

The Autoharp may be used with this song.

2. Oh, yes, we know the muffin man,
   The muffin man, the muffin man,
   Oh, yes, we know the muffin man
   Who lives in Drury Lane!

Bobby Shafto

Mother Goose

Traditional Air

Brightly

Bob - by Shaf - to's gone to sea, Sil - ver buck - les on his knee;

He'll come back and mar - ry me - - - Pret - ty Bob - by Shaf - to.

Jack and Jill

Mother Goose

J. W. Elliott

With a swing

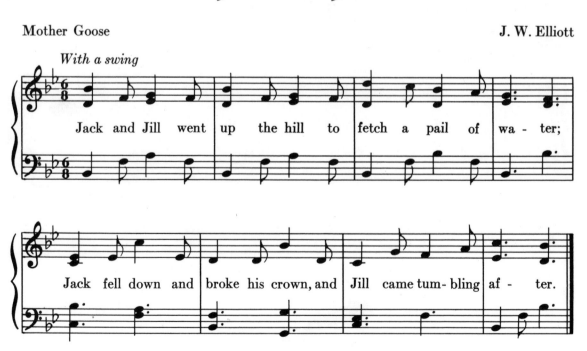

Jack and Jill went up the hill to fetch a pail of wa - ter;

Jack fell down and broke his crown, and Jill came tum-bling af - ter.

Skip to My Lou

American Folk Tune

Brightly

Skip, skip, skip to my Lou, skip, skip, skip to my Lou,

Skip, skip, skip to my Lou, Skip to my Lou, my dar - ling.

Baa! Baa! Black Sheep

Mother Goose

Traditional Air

Smoothly

"Baa! Baa! black sheep, have you an - y wool?" "Yes, sir, yes, ma'am,

three bags full; One for my mas - ter, and one for my dame, And

one for the lit - tle boy who lives in the lane."

I Love Little Pussy

Mother Goose

J. W. Elliott

Tenderly

I__ love lit - tle pus - sy, her coat is so warm, And__ if I don't hurt her, she'll do me no harm. So I'll sit by the fire __ and give her some food, And__ pus - sy will love me be - cause I am good.

The Autoharp may be used with this song.

Pop Goes the Weasel

Traditional American Folk Tune

The children form a circle, hold hands, and move around to the right as they sing. On the words "monkey stopped" they stop, squat down, and pretend to tie their shoes. At the word "pop" everyone jumps up.

The Autoharp may be used with this song.

Ten Little Indians

American Folk Air

2. Ten little, nine little, eight little Indians,
Seven little, six little, five little Indians,
Four little, three little, two little Indians,
One little Indian boy.

This is a finger play song. The children hold up both fists, the palms turned toward them. Starting with the right thumb, the corresponding number of fingers and thumbs are held up as the count goes up to ten. On the second verse, one finger is tucked away at a time, until the right thumb is left alone.

The Autoharp may be used with this song.

Little Bo-Peep

Mother Goose

J. W. Elliott

Lit - tle Bo - Peep has lost her sheep, And can't tell where _ to find them.

Leave them a - lone and they'll come home, Wag-ging their tails _ be - hind them.

Hickory, Dickory Dock

Mother Goose   J. W. Elliott

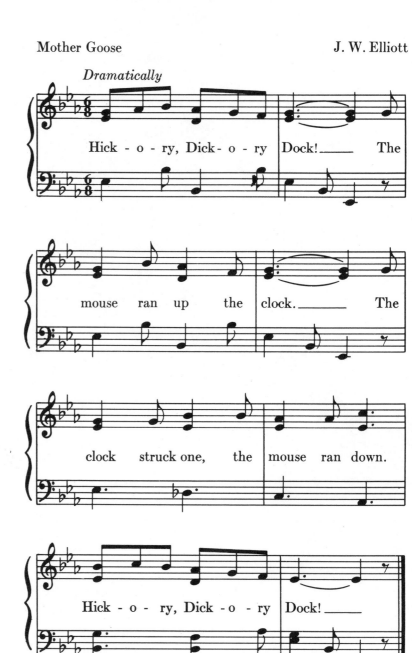

Hick - o - ry, Dick - o - ry Dock!_____ The

mouse ran up the clock._____ The

clock struck one, the mouse ran down.

Hick - o - ry, Dick - o - ry Dock!_____

Go Tell Aunt Rhody

Appalachian Folk Tune

The Autoharp may be used with this song.

2. The one she's been saving,
The one she's been saving,
The one she's been saving
To make a featherbed.

Down In the Valley

Kentucky Mountain Song

Tenderly

F

1. Down in the | val - | ley,

C7

Val - ley so | low, ____

Hang your head | o - | ver,

F

Hear the wind | blow. ____

2. Hear the wind blow, dear,
   Hear the wind blow.
   Hang your head over,
   Hear the wind blow.

The Autoharp may be used with this song.

The Farmer In the Dell

Mother Goose

Singing Game

1. The farm-er in the dell,___ The farm-er in the dell.___
Heigh, ho, the mer-ry, oh, the farm-er in the dell.___

2. The farmer takes a wife, etc.
3. The wife takes a child, etc.
4. The child takes a nurse, etc.
5. The nurse takes a dog, etc.

6. The dog takes a cat, etc.
7. The cat takes a rat, etc.
8. The rat takes the cheese, etc.
9. The cheese stands alone, etc.

A farmer is chosen to stand in the center of the circle while the other children join hands and walk around as they sing. As the second verse is sung, the farmer chooses a wife to stand beside him in the circle. As the song continues, the wife chooses a child, and so on, until the last verse. Then everyone crowds around and claps hands over the head of the "cheese."

The Autoharp may be used with this song.

Oats, Peas, Beans

Gaily

English Singing Game

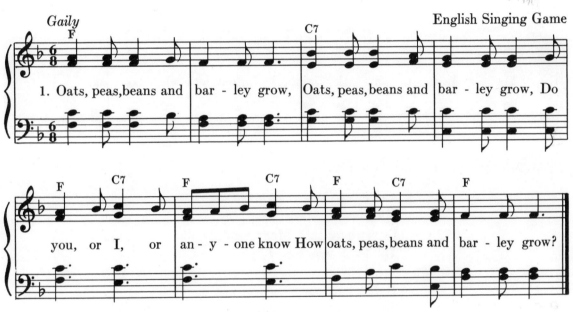

1. Oats, peas, beans and bar - ley grow, Oats, peas, beans and bar - ley grow, Do you, or I, or an - y - one know How oats, peas, beans and bar - ley grow?

2. Thus the farmer sows his seed;
   Thus he stands and takes his ease;
   He stamps his foot and claps his hand,
   And turns around to view the land.

3. Waiting for a partner,
   Waiting for a partner,
   Open the ring and take one in,
   While we all gaily dance and sing.

A circle is formed, and the children join hands and walk around as they sing. On the words "sows his seed" they pretend to scatter seed from a bag. On the words "stands and takes his ease" they stand still, hands on hips. *Etc.*

The Autoharp may be used with this song.

Mary Had a Little Lamb

Sara Josepha Hale

Traditional

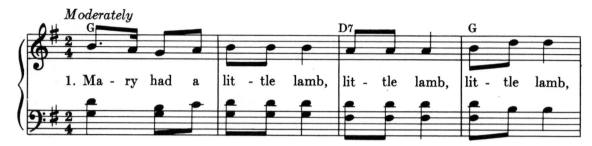

The Autoharp may be used with this song.

2. And ev'rywhere that Mary went,
   Mary went, Mary went,
   Ev'rywhere that Mary went,
   The lamb was sure to go.

3. It followed her to school one day,
   School one day, school one day,
   It followed her to school one day,
   Which was against the rule.

4. It made the children laugh and play
   Laugh and play, laugh and play,
   It made the children laugh and play,
   To see a lamb in school.

Old MacDonald Had a Farm

Old Tune

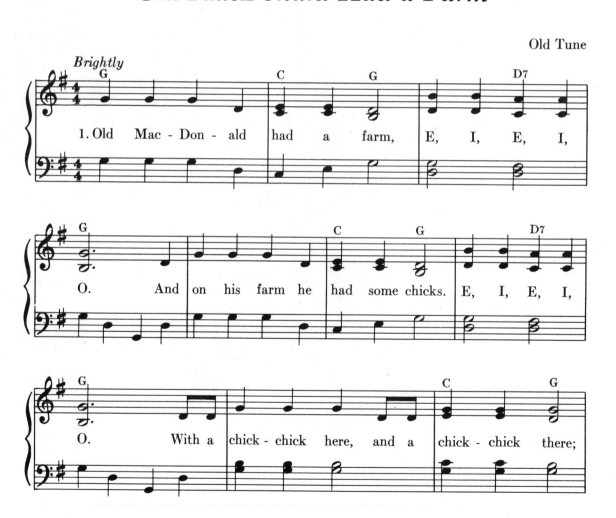

1. Old Mac-Don-ald had a farm, E, I, E, I,

O. And on his farm he had some chicks. E, I, E, I,

O. With a chick - chick here, and a chick - chick there;

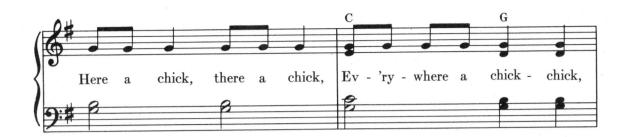

Here a chick, there a chick, Ev - 'ry - where a chick - chick,

Old Mac - Don - ald had a farm, E, I, E, I, O.

2. Ducks. Quack-quack.
3. Turkeys. Gobble-gobble.

4. Pigs. Oink-oink.
5. Cows. Moo-moo.

This is an "add-it-on" song. In the second verse, when the words, "Ev'rywhere a quack-quack," are finished, go back to "chick-chick here," and sing to the end of the song. As each succeeding animal is added, repeat the process, until at the end five different animal sounds are made, just before the grand finale.

The Autoharp may be used with this song.

Rockabye, Baby

Mother Goose

Effie Canning Carlton, 1874

Tenderly

Rock - a - bye, ba - by, on the tree top;

When the wind blows, the cra - dle will rock.

When the bough breaks, the cra - dle will fall, And

down will come ba - by, cra - dle and all!

Hop! Hop! Hop!

German Singing Game

Hop! Hop! Hop! Go and nev - er stop.

Where it's smooth, or where it's ston - y,

Trot a - long, my lit - tle pon - y.

Hop, hop, hop, hop, hop! Go and nev - er stop!

This song is fun to sing as the children drive "pretend" horses, one child in front as the horse, and another as driver, holding the reins.

The Autoharp may be used with this song.

Go In and Out the Windows

Old Tune

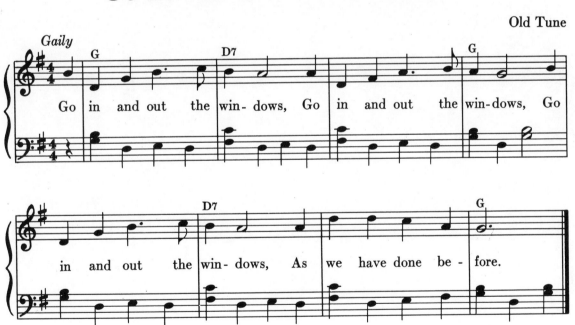

Go in and out the win-dows, Go in and out the win-dows, Go in and out the win-dows, As we have done be - fore.

A circle is formed. The children clasp hands, and raise them high to form arches. One
  child is chosen to weave in and out of the windows thus formed.

The Autoharp may be used with this song.

Ring Around A Rosy

Children's Game   Old Tune

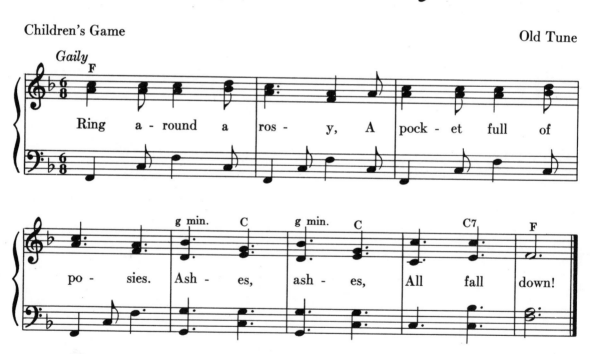

Ring a - round a ros - y, A pock - et full of po - sies. Ash - es, ash - es, All fall down!

The children form a circle, holding hands, and skip around until the word "down," when they squeal and fall down on the ground.

The Autoharp may be used with this song.

The Bear Went Over the Mountain

French tune, 18th century

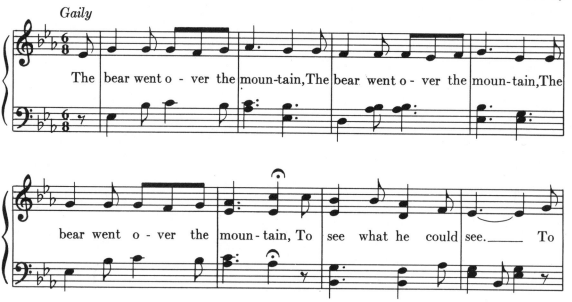

The bear went o - ver the moun-tain, The bear went o - ver the moun-tain, The

bear went o - ver the moun - tain, To see what he could see.____ To

see what he could see, ____ To see what he could see. ____ The

oth - er side of the moun - tain, The oth - er side of the moun - tain, The

oth - er side of the moun - tain Was all that he could see! ____

Itisket, Itasket

Mother Goose

Singing Game

This is an action song. A ring is formed, and one child takes a handkerchief and runs
around the outside of the ring while everyone sings. At the word "pocket," he drops
the handkerchief behind someone in the circle, and that child must catch him before
he reaches the place left vacant in the circle, or else be "it" next time.

The Autoharp may be used with this song.

Three Little Kittens

Mother Goose

Traditional Air

Smoothly

Three lit - tle kit - tens, they lost their mit - tens, And they be - gan to cry. _____ "Oh, Moth - er dear, we sad - ly fear Our mit - tens we have lost." ____ "What! Lost your mit - tens, you

The Autoharp may be used with this song.

44

Twinkle, Twinkle, Little Star!

Jane Taylor (1759-1829)

French Folk Tune

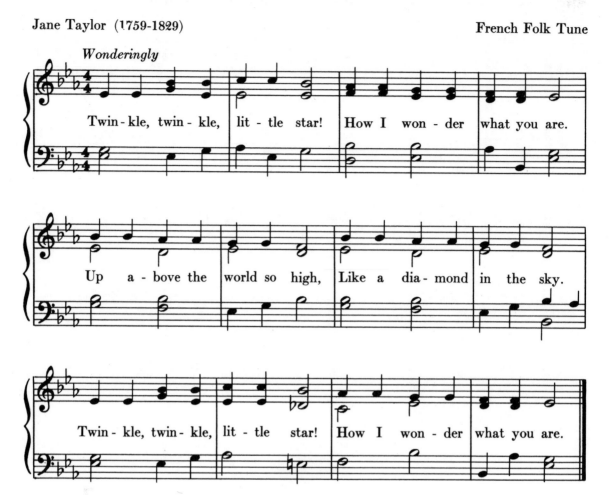

Twin - kle, twin - kle, lit - tle star! How I won - der what you are.

Up a - bove the world so high, Like a dia - mond in the sky.

Twin - kle, twin - kle, lit - tle star! How I won - der what you are.

The Autoharp may be used with this song.

She'll Be Comin' 'Round the Mountain

American Folk Tune

The Autoharp may be used with this song.

2. She'll be driving six white horses when she comes, etc.
3. Oh, we'll all go out to meet her when she comes, etc.
4. We'll be singing "Hallelujah" when she comes, etc.

A-Hunting We Will Go

Old English Singing Game

Gaily

Oh, a-hunt-ing we will go, A-hunt-ing we will go. We'll catch a fox and put him in a box, And then we'll let him go.

This song lends itself to a variety of amusing phrases. Instead of "fox . . . in a box" try substituting "whale . . . in a pail," "cat . . . in a hat" and others.

Oh, Dear, What Can the Matter Be?

Mother Goose

16th Century Air

Lightly and fast

Oh, dear, what can the mat- ter be? Dear, dear, what can the mat- ter be? Oh, dear, what can the mat- ter be? John- ny's so long at the fair. He prom-ised to bring me a bas- ket of po- sies, A gar- land of lil- ies, a

The Autoharp may be used with this song.

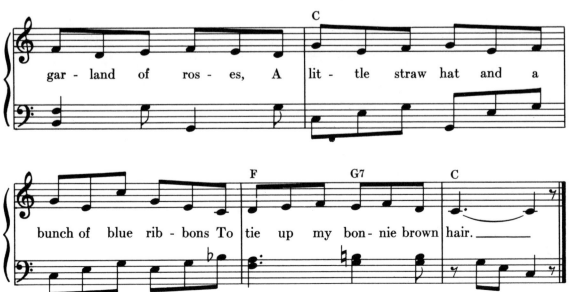

gar - land of ros - es, A lit - tle straw hat and a

bunch of blue rib - bons To tie up my bon - nie brown hair.

Looby Loo

Old English Singing Game

With steady rhythm

Here we dance loo - by loo. ____ Here we dance loo - by light. ____

Here we dance loo - by loo, ____ All on a Sat-ur-day night. ____

I put my right hand in, ____ I take my right hand out. ____ I

give my right hand a shake, shake, shake, And turn my-self a - bout. ____

2. I put my left hand in, etc.
3. I put my right foot in, etc.
4. I put my left foot in, etc.
5. I put my whole head in, etc.
6. I put my whole self in, etc.

All join hands in a circle, and move around as they sing. (As the various actions are suggested by the words, they are performed.) After each verse the circle is formed again, and the first section is sung.

The Autoharp may be used with this song.

52

Old King Cole

Mother Goose   Traditional

Old King Cole was a mer-ry old soul, And a
mer - ry old soul was he. He
called for his pipe, and he called for his bowl,
And he called for his fid - dlers three.

Jingle Bells

J. S. Pierpont

J. S. Pierpont, 1857

Jin - gle bells, jin - gle bells, Jin - gle all the way.

Oh, what fun it is to ride in a one-horse o-pen sleigh, Oh!

Jin - gle bells, jin - gle bells, Jin - gle all the way.

Oh, what fun it is to ride in a one-horse o-pen sleigh. Hey!

How D'ye Do, My Partner?

Swedish Singing Game

Cheerfully

How d'ye do, my part-ner, How d'ye do to-day?___

Will you dance in the cir-cle? I will show you the way.

Form two circles, one inside the other, by having all the children take partners, then turn and face each other. During the first four measures, the children bow or curtsy to each other twice. At "Will you dance," they join right hands, cross with left hands, and skip around the circle, singing "la, la, la" to the repeated tune. At the close, the children bow to each other, and each takes one step left, meeting a new partner, and the dance is repeated.

This singing game was found in Popular Folk Games and Dances by Mari R. Hofer, copyrighted 1907 and 1914 by A. Flanagan Co., and used with permission.

My Alphabet

Nursery Rhyme   French Folk Tune

A - B - C - D - E - F - G.   H - I - J - K - L - M - N - O - P.

Q - R - S - and T - U - V.   Doub-le you and X - Y - Z.

Now I've said my A - B - C.   Tell me what you think of me.

The Autoharp may be used with this song.

Mulberry Bush

Traditional   English Singing Game

1. Here we go round the mul-ber-ry bush, The
mul-ber-ry bush, the mul-ber-ry bush.
Here we go round the mul-ber-ry bush, So

ear - ly in ___ the morn - ing.

2. This is the way we wash our clothes,
   So early Monday morning.
3. This is the way we iron our clothes,
   So early Tuesday morning.
4. This is the way we scrub the floor,
   So early Wednesday morning.
5. This is the way we mend our clothes,
   So early Thursday morning.
6. This is the way we sweep the house,
   So early Friday morning.
7. This is the way we bake our bread,
   So early Saturday morning.
8. This is the way we go to church,
   So early Sunday morning.

The children join hands and skip around in a circle. Beginning with the second verse, they act out the words of the song. The Autoharp may be used with this song.

Are You Sleeping? (Round)
(Frère Jacques)

Steadily

French Folk Tune

This is a round, sung by two voices, or two groups of voices. When the first group reaches II, the second group begins at the beginning. Even very small children are often able to hold their parts in this song, to their great enjoyment.

The Autoharp may be used with this song.

Three Blind Mice (Round)

Mother Goose

Traditional

Three blind mice! ___ Three blind mice! ___

See how they run! ___ See how they run! ___ They

all ran af - ter the farm - er's wife, She

cut off their tails with a carv - ing knife, Did you

ev - er see such a sight in your life As three blind mice? ___

London Bridge

Mother Goose

Happily

1. Lon - don Bridge is fall - ing down, fall - ing down, fall - ing down.

Lon - don Bridge is fall - ing down, my fair la - dy.

2. Build it up with iron bars, etc.
3. Iron bars will bend and break, etc.
4. Build it up with gold and silver, etc.
5. Gold and silver I've not got, etc.
6. Here's a prisoner I have got, etc.
7. What'll you take to set him free, etc.
8. One hundred pounds will set him free, etc.
9. One hundred pounds we have not got, etc.
10. Then off to prison he must go, etc.

Two leaders are chosen to make an arch of their hands, while the other children line up
and go through the arch. At the word "Lady," the leaders drop their hands over the
child who is under the arch at that moment. The captured one is taken off to "prison"
by the leaders, as all sing "Off to prison you must go." The leaders then whisper to
the prisoner to choose between two lovely things: i.e. a diamond ring or a pearl neck-
lace. The child chooses and stands behind the leader whose gift he has chosen. When
everyone has been captured there is a tug-of-war.

The Autoharp may be used with this song.

Did You Ever See a Lassie?

Old Game Song

For very little folks. A lassie is chosen to stand before the others. Everybody sings. During the first two lines the lassie jumps, curtsies, dances, or performs what action she wishes. During the last two lines the other players imitate her.

The Autoharp may be used with this song.

Other titles in this series

Published by

RANDOM HOUSE, 457 Madison Avenue, New York 22, N. Y.

Favorite
Nursery
Songs